ULTIMATE DRUM PLAY-ALONG

FOO FIGHTERS
Play Along with 8 Great-Sounding Tracks

BOOK & PLAY-ALONG CDs
WITH **TNT** TONE 'N' TEMPO CHANGER

GW00771649

About the TNT Changer

Use the TNT software to change keys, loop playback, and mute tracks for play-along. For complete instructions, see the **TnT ReadMe.pdf** file on your enhanced CDs.

Windows users: insert a CD into your computer, double-click on My Computer, right-click on your CD drive icon, and select Explore to locate the file.

Mac users: insert a CD into your computer and double-click on the CD icon on your desktop to locate the file.

Transcriptions by Willie Rose.

Guitars and additional instrument tracks: John Allen
Bass: Al Nigro
Drums: Lee Levin

Cover photo: Steve Gullick

Produced by
Alfred Music Publishing Co., Inc.
P.O. Box 10003
Van Nuys, CA 91410-0003
alfred.com

Printed in USA.

No part of this book shall be reproduced, arranged, adapted, recorded, publicly performed, stored in a retrieval system, or transmitted by any means without written permission from the publisher. In order to comply with copyright laws, please apply for such written permission and/or license by contacting the publisher at alfred.com/permissions.

ISBN-10: 0-7390-8701-0 (Book & 2 CDs)
ISBN-13: 978-0-7390-8701-5 (Book & 2 CDs)

 Alfred Cares. Contents printed on 100% recycled paper.

Alfred

Contents

Drum Charts

ALL MY LIFE

Words and Music by
DAVID GROHL, TAYLOR HAWKINS,
CHRIS SHIFLETT and NATE MENDEL

All My Life - 9 - 1

© 2009 MJ TWELVE MUSIC, LIVING UNDER A ROCK MUSIC, I LOVE THE PUNK ROCK MUSIC and FLYING EARFORM MUSIC
All Rights for MJ TWELVE MUSIC Administered by WARNER-TAMERLANE PUBLISHING CORP.
All Rights for LIVING UNDER A ROCK MUSIC Controlled and Administered by UNIVERSAL MUSIC CORP.
All Rights for I LOVE THE PUNK ROCK MUSIC Controlled and Administered by SONGS OF UNIVERSAL, INC.
All Rights Reserved

12 *Chorus:*

EVERLONG

Words and Music by
DAVID GROHL

Everlong - 9 - 1

© 1997 MJ Twelve Music
All Rights Administered by WARNER-TAMERLANE PUBLISHING CORP.
All Rights Reserved

out of her head__ she sang.__

Come__ down,_____ and waste a - way__ with me,__

down with__ me._____

— Slow_____ how_____ you

18

Everlong - 9 - 6

20

And_ I_____ won - der

Chorus:

Everlong - 9 - 9

LEARN TO FLY

Words and Music by
DAVID GROHL, TAYLOR HAWKINS
and NATE MENDEL

Moderately fast rock ♩ = 136

Intro:

Verse 1:

Run and tell all of the an - gels, this could take_ all night._

Think-in' it in time will help_ me get_ things right._
if you give

Hook me up a new rev - o - lu - tion, 'cause

Learn to Fly - 7 - 1

© 1999 MJ TWELVE MUSIC, LIVING UNDER A ROCK MUSIC and FLYING EARFORM MUSIC
All Rights for MJ TWELVE MUSIC Administered by WARNER-TAMERLANE PUBLISHING CORP.
All Rights for LIVING UNDER A ROCK MUSIC Controlled and Administered by UNIVERSAL MUSIC CORP.
All Rights Reserved

MONKEY WRENCH

Words and Music by
DAVID GROHL, TAYLOR HAWKINS
and NATE MENDEL

Fast rock ♩ = 174

Intro:

Verse 1:

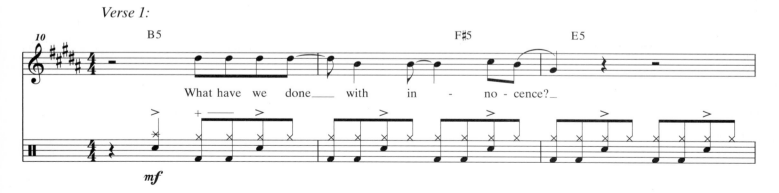

What have we done___ with in - no - cence?___

Monkey Wrench - 8 - 1

© 1999 MJ TWELVE MUSIC, LIVING UNDER A ROCK MUSIC and FLYING EARFORM MUSIC
All Rights for MJ TWELVE MUSIC Administered by WARNER-TAMERLANE PUBLISHING CORP.
All Rights for LIVING UNDER A ROCK MUSIC Controlled and Administered by UNIVERSAL MUSIC CORP.
All Rights Reserved

It dis - ap - peared— with time,— it nev - er made— much sense.—

Ad - o - les - - cent res - i - dent.—

Wast-ing an - oth - - er night— on plan-ning my— re - venge.—

Pre-chorus:

One in ten.——

One in ten.—

One in ten.——

Verse 2:

All this time___ to make___ a - mends.___

What do you do___when all___ your en - e - mies___ are friends?___

Now and then,___ I'll try___ to bend.___

Un - der pres - sure, wind___ up snap-ping in___ the end.___

Pre-chorus:

One in ten.___

One in ten.___ One in ten.___

34

Tem - per.

Verse 3:

One last thing be - fore I quit! I nev - er want - ed an - y more than

I could fit in - to my head! I still re - mem - ber ev - 'ry sin - gle

word you said, and all the shit that some - how came a - long with it! Still,

there's one thing that com - forts me since I was al - ways caged and now I'm

MY HERO

Words and Music by
DAVID GROHL, NATE MENDEL
and PAT SMEAR

Moderately fast rock ♩ = 154 (w/half-time feel)

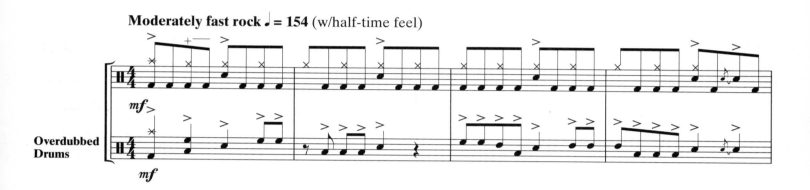

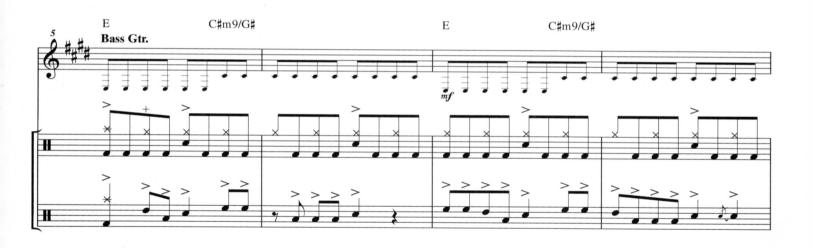

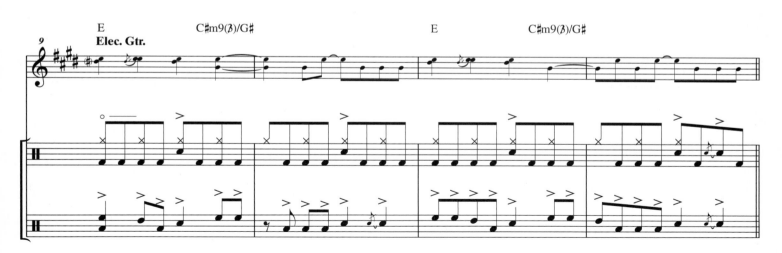

My Hero - 7 - 1

© 1997 MJ TWELVE MUSIC, SONGS OF KOBALT MUSIC PUBLISHING,
FLYING EARFORM MUSIC and RUTHENSMEAR MUSIC (Administered by BUG MUSIC)
All Rights for MJ TWELVE MUSIC Administered by WARNER-TAMERLANE PUBLISHING CORP.
All Rights Reserved

Chorus:

There goes my he - ro.__ Watch him as__ he goes.__

There goes my he - ro.__ He's or-di - nar - y.__

THE PRETENDER

Words and Music by
DAVID GROHL, TAYLOR HAWKINS,
CHRIS SHIFLETT and NATE MENDEL

Fast ♩ = 175
Half-time feel
Intro:

Keep you___ in___ the___ dark.___ You know___ they all_____ pre - tend.

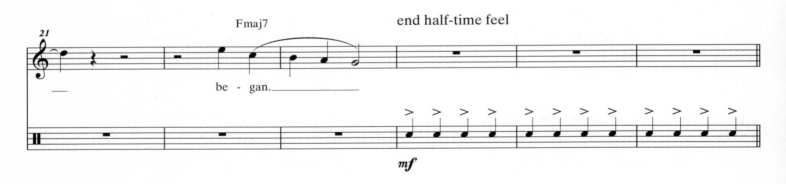

Keep you___ in_____ the___ dark,___ and so___ it all___

___ be - gan._____

end half-time feel

mf

The Pretender - 10 - 1

© 2007 SONGS OF UNIVERSAL, INC, MJ TWELVE MUSIC,
LIVING UNDER A ROCK MUSIC, I LOVE THE PUNK ROCK MUSIC and FLYING EARFORM MUSIC
All Rights for MJ TWELVE MUSIC and I LOVE THE PUNK ROCK MUSIC Controlled and Administered by SONGS OF UNIVERSAL, INC.
All Rights for LIVING UNDER A ROCK MUSIC Controlled and Administered by UNIVERSAL MUSIC CORP.
All Rights for FLYING EARFORM MUSIC Administered by BUG MUSIC
This Arrangement © 2011 SONGS OF UNIVERSAL, INC, MJ TWELVE MUSIC,
LIVING UNDER A ROCK MUSIC, I LOVE THE PUNK ROCK MUSIC and FLYING EARFORM MUSIC
All Rights Reserved
Reprinted by Permission of Hal Leonard Corporation

Verse 1:

Chorus:

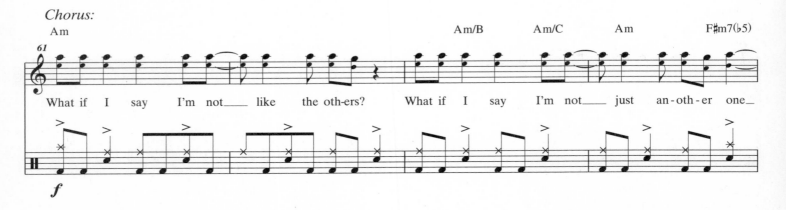

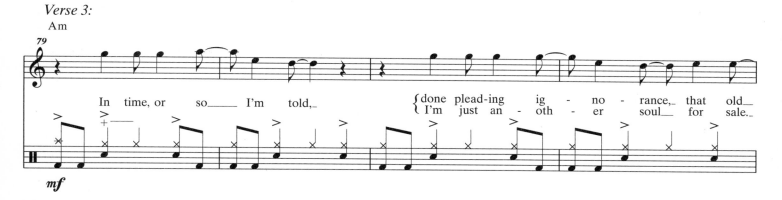

Verse 3:

The Pretender - 10 - 4

48

The lyrics within the sheet music:

de - fense.
Oh, well.

The page___ is out___ of print. We are___ not per-
The page___ is out___ of print.

- ma - nent,_ we're tem - po - rar - y, tem - po -

rar - y. Same___ old sto - ry.

Chorus:

What if I say I'm not___ like the oth-ers? What if I say I'm not___ just an-oth-er one___

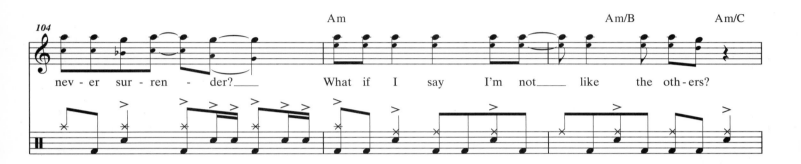

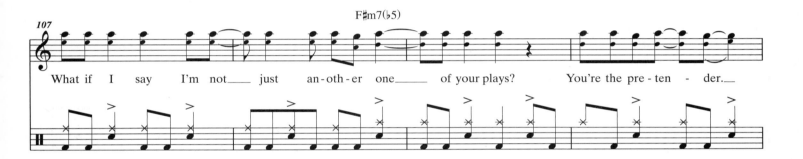

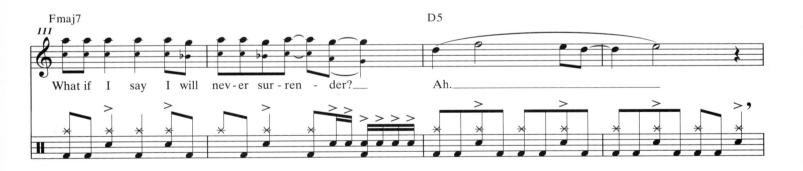

Bridge:

52

Chorus:

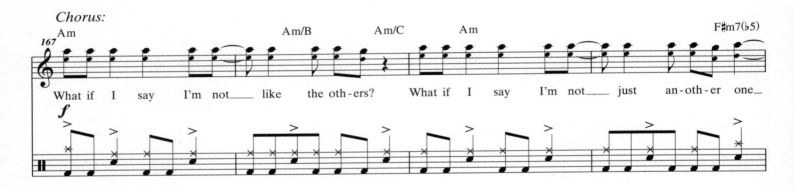

The Pretender - 10 - 9

TIMES LIKE THESE

Words and Music by
DAVID GROHL, TAYLOR HAWKINS,
CHRIS SHIFLETT and NATE MENDEL

Moderate rock ♩ = 144

Intro:
Elec. Gtr.

Times Like These - 8 - 1

© 2002 MJ TWELVE MUSIC, LIVING UNDER A ROCK MUSIC, I LOVE THE PUNK ROCK MUSIC and FLYING EARFORM MUSIC
All Rights for MJ TWELVE MUSIC Administered by WARNER-TAMERLANE PUBLISHING CORP.
All Rights for LIVING UNDER A ROCK MUSIC Controlled and Administered by UNIVERSAL MUSIC CORP.
All Rights for I LOVE THE PUNK ROCK MUSIC Controlled and Administered by SONGS OF UNIVERSAL, INC.
All Rights Reserved

Verse 1:

Times Like These - 8 - 2

Verse 2:

I,
I'm a new day ris - ing,
I'm a brand - new sky_____ to hang_____ the stars_____ up - on_____ to - night.

But I,_____
I'm a lit - tle di - vid - ed. Do I stay_____ or run_____
_____ a - way_____ and leave_____ it all_____ be - hind?_____
and_____

60

Chorus:

It's times___ like these___ you learn___ to live___ a - gain. It's times___ like these___ you give___ and give___ a - gain. It's times___ like these___ you learn___ to love___ a - gain. It's times___ like these___ time___ and time___ a - gain. It's times___ like these___ you learn___ to live___ a - gain, It's times___

WALK

Words and Music by
DAVID GROHL, TAYLOR HAWKINS,
CHRIS SHIFLETT, NATE MENDEL
and PAT SMEAR

Walk - 8 - 1

© 2007 SONGS OF UNIVERSAL, INC., MJ TWELVE MUSIC, LIVING UNDER A ROCK MUSIC,
I LOVE THE PUNK ROCK MUSIC, FLYING EARFORM MUSIC and RUTHENSMEAR MUSIC (Administered by BUG MUSIC)
All Rights for MJ TWELVE MUSIC and I LOVE THE PUNK ROCK MUSIC Controlled and Administered by SONGS OF UNIVERSAL, INC.
All Rights for LIVING UNDER A ROCK MUSIC Controlled and Administered by UNIVERSAL MUSIC CORP.
All Rights for FLYING EARFORM MUSIC and RUTHENSMEAR MUSIC Administered by BUG MUSIC
This Arrangement © 2011 SONGS OF UNIVERSAL, INC., MJ TWELVE MUSIC, LIVING UNDER A ROCK MUSIC,
I LOVE THE PUNK ROCK MUSIC, FLYING EARFORM MUSIC and RUTHENSMEAR MUSIC
All Rights Reserved
Reprinted by Permission of Hal Leonard Corporation

Chorus:

64

Walk - 8 - 3

Walk - 8 - 8

ALL MY LIFE

Words and Music by
DAVID GROHL, TAYLOR HAWKINS,
CHRIS SHIFLETT and NATE MENDEL

All My Life - 4 - 1

© 2009 MJ TWELVE MUSIC, LIVING UNDER A ROCK MUSIC, I LOVE THE PUNK ROCK MUSIC and FLYING EARFORM MUSIC
All Rights for MJ TWELVE MUSIC Administered by WARNER-TAMERLANE PUBLISHING CORP.
All Rights for LIVING UNDER A ROCK MUSIC Controlled and Administered by UNIVERSAL MUSIC CORP.
All Rights for I LOVE THE PUNK ROCK MUSIC Controlled and Administered by SONGS OF UNIVERSAL, INC.
All Rights Reserved

Verse 2:

mf

Chorus:

f

72

Interlude:

Bridge:

mf

Chorus:

Outro:

All My Life - 4 - 4

EVERLONG

Words and Music by
DAVID GROHL

Moderately fast rock ♩ = 158

Everlong - 5 - 1

© 1997 MJ TWELVE MUSIC
All Rights Administered by WARNER-TAMERLANE PUBLISHING CORP.
All Rights Reserved

Verse 2:

Pre-chorus:

78

LEARN TO FLY

Words and Music by
DAVID GROHL, TAYLOR HAWKINS
and NATE MENDEL

Moderately fast rock ♩ = 136

Learn to Fly - 3 - 1

© 1999 MJ TWELVE MUSIC, LIVING UNDER A ROCK MUSIC and FLYING EARFORM MUSIC
All Rights for MJ TWELVE MUSIC Administered by WARNER-TAMERLANE PUBLISHING CORP.
All Rights for LIVING UNDER A ROCK MUSIC Controlled and Administered by UNIVERSAL MUSIC CORP.
All Rights Reserved

MONKEY WRENCH

Words and Music by
DAVID GROHL, TAYLOR HAWKINS
and NATE MENDEL

Monkey Wrench - 4 - 1

© 1999 MJ TWELVE MUSIC, LIVING UNDER A ROCK MUSIC and FLYING EARFORM MUSIC
All Rights for MJ TWELVE MUSIC Administered by WARNER-TAMERLANE PUBLISHING CORP.
All Rights for LIVING UNDER A ROCK MUSIC Controlled and Administered by UNIVERSAL MUSIC CORP.
All Rights Reserved

84

Monkey Wrench - 4 - 3

Monkey Wrench - 4 - 4

MY HERO

Words and Music by
DAVID GROHL, NATE MENDEL
and PAT SMEAR

My Hero - 5 - 1

© 1997 MJ TWELVE MUSIC, SONGS OF KOBALT MUSIC PUBLISHING,
FLYING EARFORM MUSIC and RUTHENSMEAR MUSIC (Administered by BUG MUSIC)
All Rights for MJ TWELVE MUSIC Administered by WARNER-TAMERLANE PUBLISHING CORP.
All Rights Reserved

88

Verse 2:

Chorus:

Interlude:

Verse 3:

Chorus:

THE PRETENDER

Words and Music by
DAVID GROHL, TAYLOR HAWKINS,
CHRIS SHIFLETT and NATE MENDEL

The Pretender - 4 - 1

© 2007 SONGS OF UNIVERSAL, INC., MJ TWELVE MUSIC,
LIVING UNDER A ROCK MUSIC, I LOVE THE PUNK ROCK MUSIC and FLYING EARFORM MUSIC
All Rights for MJ TWELVE MUSIC and I LOVE THE PUNK ROCK MUSIC Controlled and Administered by SONGS OF UNIVERSAL, INC.
All Rights for LIVING UNDER A ROCK MUSIC Controlled and Administered by UNIVERSAL MUSIC CORP.
All Rights for FLYING EARFORM MUSIC Administered by BUG MUSIC
This Arrangement © 2011 SONGS OF UNIVERSAL, INC., MJ TWELVE MUSIC,
LIVING UNDER A ROCK MUSIC, I LOVE THE PUNK ROCK MUSIC and FLYING EARFORM MUSIC
All Rights Reserved
Reprinted by Permission of Hal Leonard Corporation

Bridge: (m. 119)

94 *Chorus:*

TIMES LIKE THESE

Words and Music by
DAVID GROHL, TAYLOR HAWKINS,
CHRIS SHIFLETT and NATE MENDEL

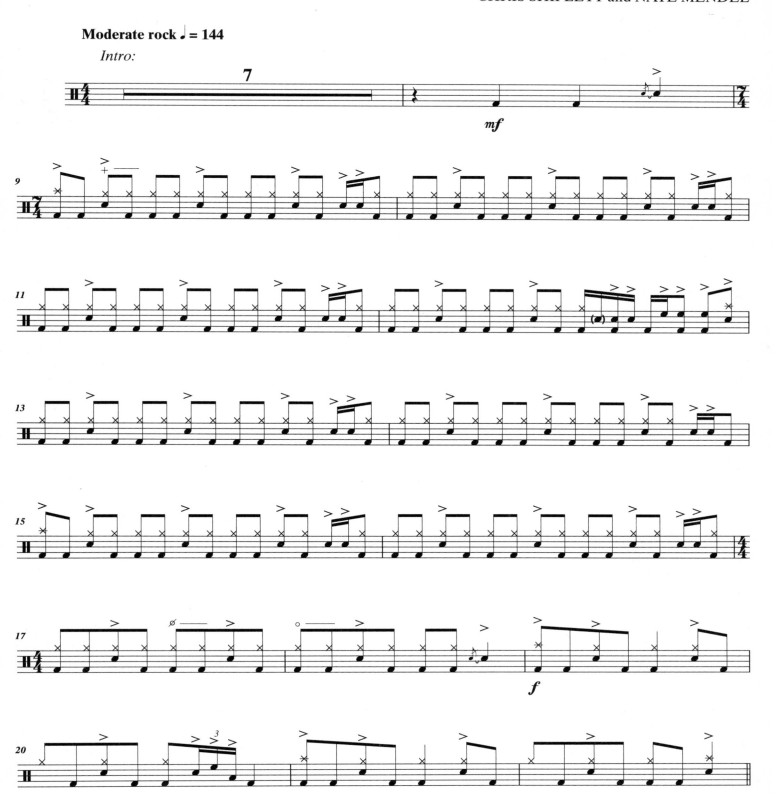

Times Like These - 5 - 1

© 2002 MJ TWELVE MUSIC, LIVING UNDER A ROCK MUSIC, I LOVE THE PUNK ROCK MUSIC and FLYING EARFORM MUSIC
All Rights for MJ TWELVE MUSIC Administered by WARNER-TAMERLANE PUBLISHING CORP.
All Rights for LIVING UNDER A ROCK MUSIC Controlled and Administered by UNIVERSAL MUSIC CORP.
All Rights for I LOVE THE PUNK ROCK MUSIC Controlled and Administered by SONGS OF UNIVERSAL, INC.
All Rights Reserved

98

Interlude:

mf

(o)

f

Times Like These - 5 - 4

Chorus:

Outro:

WALK

Words and Music by
DAVID GROHL, TAYLOR HAWKINS,
CHRIS SHIFLETT, NATE MENDEL
and PAT SMEAR

Walk - 4 - 1

© 2007 SONGS OF UNIVERSAL, INC., MJ TWELVE MUSIC, LIVING UNDER A ROCK MUSIC,
I LOVE THE PUNK ROCK MUSIC, FLYING EARFORM MUSIC and RUTHENSMEAR MUSIC (Administered by BUG MUSIC)
All Rights for MJ TWELVE MUSIC and I LOVE THE PUNK ROCK MUSIC Controlled and Administered by SONGS OF UNIVERSAL, INC.
All Rights for LIVING UNDER A ROCK MUSIC Controlled and Administered by UNIVERSAL MUSIC CORP.
All Rights for FLYING EARFORM MUSIC and RUTHENSMEAR MUSIC Administered by BUG MUSIC
This Arrangement © 2011 SONGS OF UNIVERSAL, INC., MJ TWELVE MUSIC, LIVING UNDER A ROCK MUSIC,
I LOVE THE PUNK ROCK MUSIC, FLYING EARFORM MUSIC and RUTHENSMEAR MUSIC
All Rights Reserved
Reprinted by Permission of Hal Leonard Corporation

Chorus:

$\boldsymbol{f}$

102 *Bridge:*

Chorus:

Walk - 4 - 3

DRUM KEY

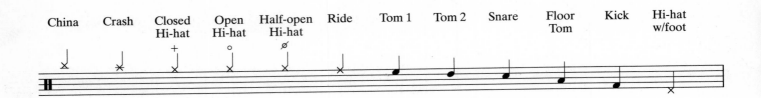